# The Blend Tree

Look at the words on the apples. If you see a **blend** at the beginning of the word, color the apple red. If you see a **blend** at the end of the word, color the apple yellow. Then color the rest of the picture.

Recognizing consonant blends: initial and final position

# A Barn on a Farm

Usually, **ar** has the vowel sound you hear in **barn**.

**barn**

Circle the correct name for each picture.

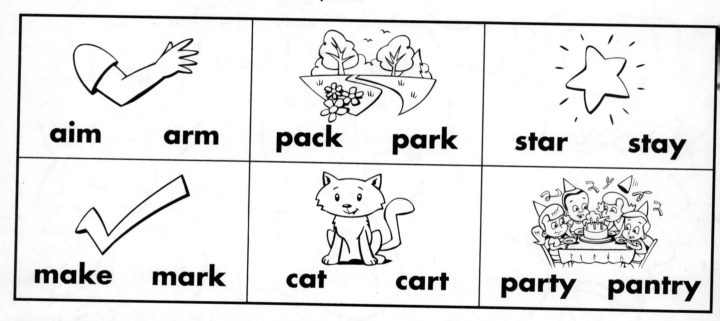

| | | |
|---|---|---|
| **aim**    **arm** | **pack**    **park** | **star**    **stay** |
| **make**    **mark** | **cat**    **cart** | **party**    **pantry** |

Write **ar** to complete each word below. Then read the words aloud.

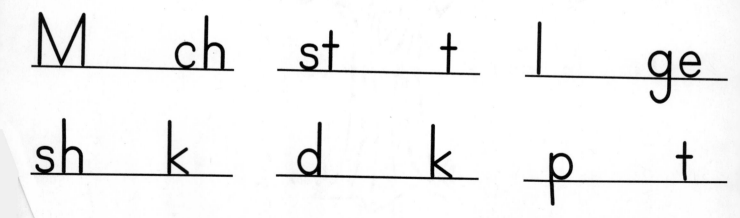

M___  ch___  st___t  l___ge

sh___k  d___k  p___t

# Blow Your Horn for or!

Usually, **or** has the vowel sound you hear in **horn**.

h**or**n

Circle the correct name for each picture.

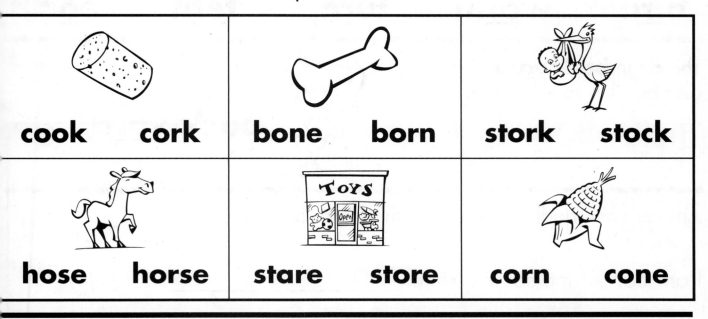

cook    cork

bone    born

stork    stock

hose    horse

stare    store

corn    cone

Write **or** to complete each word on the left. Then draw lines to match each **or** word with its opposite.

m ___ e

sh ___ t

bef ___ e

n ___ th

st ___ my

**tall**

**sunny**

**after**

**less**

**south**

# The Early Bird Gets the Worm

The vowel sound is the same in each of the words below.

**b<u>ir</u>d**   **w<u>or</u>m**   **t<u>ur</u>n**   **f<u>er</u>n**   **<u>ear</u>th**

---

The **ar** in **backward**
also has this vowel sound.

   **backw<u>ar</u>d**

---

Answer each riddle using one of the words from above.

I am part of the solar system. _____

I live in the dirt. _____

I like to chirp. _____

I am the opposite of forward. _____

---

Circle the words that have the same vowel sound that you hear in **<u>ear</u>th**.

**nurse**        **fur**        **four**        **forward**

**burn**        **more**        **girl**        **word**

Recognizing the sounds of **r**-controlled vowels

# Different Letters, Same Sound

Usually, **aw** and **au** have the same vowel sound you hear in the words **saw** and **automobile**.

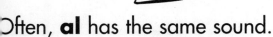

**automobile**

Often, **al** has the same sound.

**call**

**talk**

Read the words in the box. Circle the letters that stand for the same vowel sound in each word. Write a word from the box to name each picture.

| salt | walk | ball | yawn | haul | hawk |
|------|------|------|------|------|------|

_____

_____

_____

_____

# How About ow and ou?

Both **ow** and **ou** can have the same vowel sound.

br**ow**n  r**ou**nd

Read each word. Underline **ow** or **ou** in each word.

| how | about | loud | flower |
|---|---|---|---|

cowboy      house      down      mouth      found

Read each sentence. Circle the words that are misspelled and rewrite them correctly on the lines.

**The cloun likes to laugh and showt.**

_____  _____

**The couboy sniffs the flour.**

_____  _____

**Nou we will sit on the grownd.**

_____  _____

Recognizing the diphthongs **ow** and **ou**

# Ought We to Trust ou?

There are different sounds for **ou**. Say each word below and listen for the **ou** sound.

| **c**<u>**ou**</u>**ld** | **c**<u>**ou**</u>**ch** | **c**<u>**ou**</u>**gh** |

When **ou** is followed by **ght**, the **gh** is silent and only the **t** is heard.

## She b<u>ou</u>ght skates.

Color the two boxes in each row whose words share the same **ou** sound.

| about | ought | bought |
|-------|-------|--------|
| would | found | could |
| mouth | out | would |
| cough | fought | should |

# Looking at oo

In some words, **oo** has the vowel sound you hear in the word **l<u>oo</u>k**.

**l<u>oo</u>k**

**h<u>oo</u>d**

**br<u>oo</u>k**

Match each word with its picture.

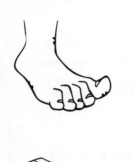

**book**

**cookie**

**foot**

**hood**

**hook**

**wood**

Underline each word with the same vowel sound as **f<u>oo</u>t**.

**stood**     **took**     **tooth**     **good**     **boot**     **look**

# Some Special Words

The words in the box below all have the same vowel sound as **look**. Read each word and underline the letter or letters that stand for the vowel sound you hear in **look**.

| | | |
|---|---|---|
| could | would | bull |
| put | should | full |

The **l** in the words **could**, **would**, and **should** is silent—it has no sound.

---

Circle the word that best completes each sentence. Write the word on the line.

The box is _____ of pens.

| | |
|---|---|
| full | pull |

The big _____ has horns.

| | |
|---|---|
| bull | could |

You _____ be kind to pets.

| | |
|---|---|
| should | would |

I _____ my bike away.

| | |
|---|---|
| pull | put |

# The Joyful Noise of oi and oy!

Both **oi** and **oy** have the same vowel sound.

 **b<u>oy</u>**

 **b<u>oi</u>l**

Read each word. Underline **oi** or **oy** in each word.

| oil | choice | noise | point |
|-----|--------|-------|-------|
| join | annoy | toy | joy |

Read each sentence. Circle the words that have the same sound you hear in the word **boy**. Write the words on the lines.

**Roy will boil a hot dog.**

_____   _____

**An oyster will not spoil.**

_____   _____

**The cowboy lost his ten coins.**

_____   _____

# A Moose on the Moon

In some words, **oo** has the vowel sound you hear in **m<u>oo</u>n**.

**m<u>oo</u>n**

**moose**

**f<u>oo</u>d**

---

Read each word. Match each word with its picture.

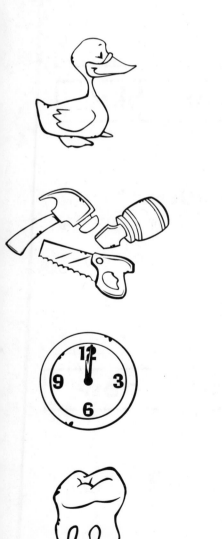

**boot**

**goose**

**noon**

**roof**

**tools**

**tooth**

**balloon**

**igloo**

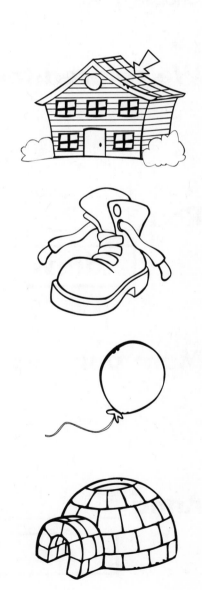

Recognizing the long double **o** sound of **oo**

**11**

# Let's Buy Some New Glue

Often, **ew** and **ue** have the same vowel sound as the **oo** in m**oo**n.

**New Glue on *Sale!***

n**ew**          gl**ue**

Choose a word that best completes each sentence and write it on the line.

**We colored the sky** _____.

| blew | bloom | blue |

**Ron** _____ **a picture.**

| drew | droop | due |

**Mom put meat in the** _____.

| clue | gloom | stew |

**Anna** _____ **the ball.**

| true | threw | troop |

Recognizing the long double **o** sound of **ew** and **ue**

# You're Making Contractions

A **contraction** is two words put together. One or more letters are left out. In their place is this mark **'** called **an apostrophe**.

apostrophe →

she will = she + ~~will~~ = **she'll**

**She'll** eat vegetables anytime!

Draw a line to match each pair of words with its **contraction**.

he will

I am

you are

we would

she is

can not

we'd

he'll

I'm

she's

can't

you're

# Nice Ice

Every **statement** ends with a **period**.
    I like the shiny ice.

Every **question** ends with a **question mark**.
    Do you think the ice is nice?

Put a **period** or **question mark** at the end of each sentence.

### The day is cold_____

### Did the lake freeze_____

### Bob has a new hat_____

### Who will win the race_____

### Can you ice skate_____

### The dog slips_____

Using correct punctuation with statements and questions

# Awesome!

A sentence that shows excitement is called an **exclamation**.
Every **exclamation** begins with a capital letter and ends with an
**exclamation point**.

capital letter

## **<u>W</u>atch out<u>!</u>**

exclamation point

---

Read each sentence. Circle the sentences that express excitement.

**I was scared!**

**What time is it?**

**I see the ice cream truck!**

---

Fill in the ◯ by the **exclamation** that is written correctly.

◯ **The soup is hot!**
◯ **the soup is hot.**

◯ **My toe hurts.**
◯ **My toe hurts!**

◯ **Look at the sun setting!**
◯ **Is the sun setting?**

# Start with a Capital

The first word in a sentence always begins with a **capital** letter.

**This pig is fat.**

**The store is open.**

Rewrite each sentence correctly.

**cake is yummy.**

_____

**use a pen to write.**

_____

**bill digs a hole.**

_____

**the pin is sharp!**

_____

**my fish's name is Goldy.**

_____

**this peach is very juicy.**

_____

Using a capital letter at the beginning of a sentence

# Proper Nouns Use Capitals

A **proper noun** is the name of a specific person, place, or thing. Your name is a **proper noun**.

Every **proper noun** begins with a capital letter.

**<u>U</u>nited <u>S</u>tates**          **<u>J</u>une**

Underline the **proper noun** in each sentence that is not written correctly.

The train goes to boston.

maria ran home.

was born on june 2, 1997.

this man lives in japan.

My cat's name is misty.

ken has a red bike.

# How Many?

A **noun** that names "more than one" is a **plural noun**.
To make many **nouns** mean "more than one," add **s** at the end.

**one bear**          **three bears**

Look at the picture. Then read the questions and circle the answers.

**1. Look for a cap. How many do you see?**

| one cap | two caps | three caps |

**2. Look for a rope. How many do you see?**

| one rope | two ropes | three ropes |

**3. Look for a mat. How many do you see?**

| one mat | two mats | three mats |

**4. Look for a ball. How many do you see?**

| one ball | two balls | three balls |

Forming plurals of regular nouns by adding **s**

# Not Just One

Ad **es** to a **noun** ending in **s**, **x**, **ch**, or **sh** to make it a **plural noun**.

**one dress**  **two dress<u>es</u>**  **one fox**  **two fox<u>es</u>**

Rewrite each **noun**, adding **es** at the end to make it **plural**.

**match** _____

**bus** _____

**brush** _____

**box** _____

**glass** _____

# Changes for y

Sometimes **y** comes after a consonant at the end of a **noun**.
To make these nouns **plural**, change the **y** to **i** and add **es**.

**one bunny**   bunn~~y~~ **i** + **es** = **bunnies**   **two bunnies**

Rewrite each **noun** to make it **plural**.

**candy**

**fly**

**baby**

**berry**

**kitty**

**lady**

# Making Plurals

Read the **nouns** inside the ◇s. Circle the correct **plural** form of each one.

daisy — daisies / daisys

cherry — cherries / cherryes

lunch — lunchs / lunches

fly — flies / flyes

fox — foxs / foxes

city — cityes / cities

chick — chickes / chicks

puppy — puppies / puppys

# Special Plurals

Some **nouns** have a special **plural** form.

| One | More Than One |
|-----|---------------|
| man | men |
| woman | women |
| child | children |
| mouse | mice |
| foot | feet |
| tooth | teeth |

Write the **plural** form of the **noun** in the box to complete each sentence.

 I have two _____ . foot

Both _____ can swim. child

The _____ like the maze. mouse

Two _____ wrote the song. man

I brush my _____ . tooth

Three _____ baked pies. woman

Recognizing irregular plurals

# More Special Plurals

A few **nouns** do not change in their **plural** form.

| One | More Than One |
| --- | --- |
| deer | deer |
| fish | fish |
| moose | moose |
| scissors | scissors |
| sheep | sheep |

Look at the picture clues. Write the missing **plural noun** in each sentence.

**Many** _____ **live in the park.**

**Luis saw two** _____ **in the woods.**

**The** _____ **eat grass.**

**Feed the** _____ **before lunch.**

**Use** _____ **to cut paper.**

*Recognizing irregular plurals*

# Bears in Space

A **verb** usually ends in **s** when it tells about only one.
It usually does not end in **s** when it tells about more than one.

One star **twinkle<u>s</u>**.      Stars **twinkle**.

Circle the correct **verb** to complete each sentence. Then color the picture.

**Young Bear _____ a helmet.**

| wear | wears |
|------|-------|

**Mom and Dad Bear _____ photos.**

| take | takes |
|------|-------|

**They all _____ in space.**

| floats | float |
|--------|-------|

**Young Bear _____ space.**

| likes | like |
|-------|------|

**Mom and Dad Bear _____ space, too.**

| likes | like |
|-------|------|

     Choosing the correct verb form to agree with the subject

# Which Sounds Correct?

Read each sentence. Fill in the ○ by the sentence that uses the correct **verb**.

○The children like art.
○The children likes art.

○Maria paint a flower.
○Maria paints a flower.

○A boy use clay.
○A boy uses clay.

○Two boys draw cars.
○Two boys draws cars.

○The teacher hangs up the art.
○The teacher hang up the art.

○They all works hard.
○They all work hard.

# Am, Are, and Is

Verbs may also tell what a person or thing is. We use the verbs **am**, **are**, and **is** to do this.

## Verb Chart

| | |
|---|---|
| I – – – – – – – – – | **am** |
| You – – – – – – – – | **are** |
| He, She, or It – – – – | **is** |
| We – – – – – – – – | **are** |
| They – – – – – – – | **are** |

Use **am** with **I** when you tell about yourself.

I **am** happy!

Use **is** with **he**, **she**, or **it** when you tell about another person or thing.

He **is** happy!

Use **are** with **you** or when you tell about more than one.

The dogs **are** happy!

Write **am**, **are**, or **is** to complete each sentence.

Leaves _____ green.          I _____ smart.

Nan _____ a girl.          Candy _____ sweet.

We _____ friends.          You _____ nice.

# You Are Smart!

Read each sentence. Fill in the ◯ by the sentence that uses the correct **verb**.

◯I am your friend.
◯I is your friend.

◯You is the winner!
◯You are the winner!

◯Brian is a good kicker.
◯Brian are a good kicker.

◯The puppy is tiny.
◯The puppy are tiny.

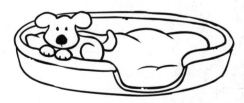

◯We are sleepy.
◯We is sleepy.

# Has or Have?

**Verbs** may also tell what a person or thing has.
We use the verbs **has** and **have** to do this.

Use **has** with **he, she,** or **it**.
Use **has** with a noun that names one.

He **has** a tail.
The squirrel **has** a tail.

We **have** tails!

Use **have** with **I**, **you**,
**we**, or **they**.
Use **have** with a plural noun.

They **have** tails.
The squirrels **have** tails.

| has | have |
|---|---|
| he, she, it | I, you, we, they |
| noun | plural noun |

Read each sentence. Fill in the ○ by the sentence that uses the correct **verb**.

○ A dog **has** a tail.
○ A dog **have** a tail.

○ He **has** a new bike.
○ He **have** a new bike.

○ They **have** gone home.
○ They **has** gone home.

○ Birds **has** wings.
○ Birds **have** wings.

# Have Fun!

Write **has** or **have** to complete each sentence.

The panda _____ a baby.

Nuts _____ hard shells.

He _____ broken the law.

The shaker _____ salt in it.

They _____ launched the rocket.

The crabs _____ claws.

# Does and Do

Use **does** with **he**, **she**, or **it**.
Use **does** with a noun that names one.

He **does** his job.
The man **does** his job.

"You **do** a good job!"

Use **do** with **I**, **you**, **we**, or **they**.
Use **do** with a plural noun.

They **do** good work.
The people **do** good work.

| does | do |
|------|-----|
| he, she, it | I, you, we, they |
| noun | plural noun |

Write **does** or **do** to complete each sentence.

Children _____ like to play games.

She _____ tricks.

I _____ my homework.

Tim _____ his chores.

Using **does** and **do**: present tense forms of the verb **to do**

# Do Your Best!

Write **does** or **do** to complete each sentence.

This hat _____ not have stripes.

Fairies _____ magic.

Mom _____ like to read.

Clowns _____ funny tricks.

Ann _____ skate well.

Tom _____ like to eat cake.

# Let's Go to the Movies!

Write a **noun** or **verb** from the box to complete each sentence.

| box | buy | is | meet | seats |
|-----|-----|-----|------|-------|

Rita and Tom _____ at the door.
**verb**

They _____ tickets.
**verb**

They buy a _____ of popcorn.
**noun**

They choose their _____ .
**noun**

The movie _____ funny.
**verb**

Completing sentences with **nouns** and **verbs**

# Pete and Pat

Read the short story.
Circle the correct **noun** or **verb**
to complete each sentence.
Then color the picture.

Pete (has  have) a dog. The dog (is  am) tan and black. Her name is Pat.

Pat (like  likes) to run. Her (tail  tails) wags when she (run  runs). Pat likes to chew (bone  bones). Pete (give  gives) her a bone every (day  dry). Pat likes to (plays  play). Pete throws a (ball  bull) to her. Pat likes that (game  gum).

Pat (love  loves) Pete. Pete (loves  love) Pat. They are best (friends  friend).

# Words that Describe

Some words tell more about nouns.
They are called **adjectives**.
**Adjectives** can answer these questions:

What kind?
**fuzzy** bears

How many?
**two** bears

What color?
**white** bears

Read each sentence. Circle the **adjective** in each sentence.

**This is a pretty flower.**
**It has two leaves.**

**I see tiny mice.**
**I see three mice.**

**She has long hair.**
**She has big eyes.**

**The bus is big.**
**The wheels are black.**

　　　　Recognizing adjectives

# A Sunny Afternoon

**Adjectives** tell more about nouns.

Write an **adjective** from the box to complete each sentence.

| sleepy | two | black | four |

A _____ bird sings.
**What color?**

There are _____ clouds.
**How many?**

A _____ dog takes a nap.
**What kind?**

I see _____ squirrels.
**How many?**

*Choosing adjectives to complete sentences*

# Tell About a Toy

Write the name of a toy you like in the square.
Write an **adjective** that tells about the toy in each circle.

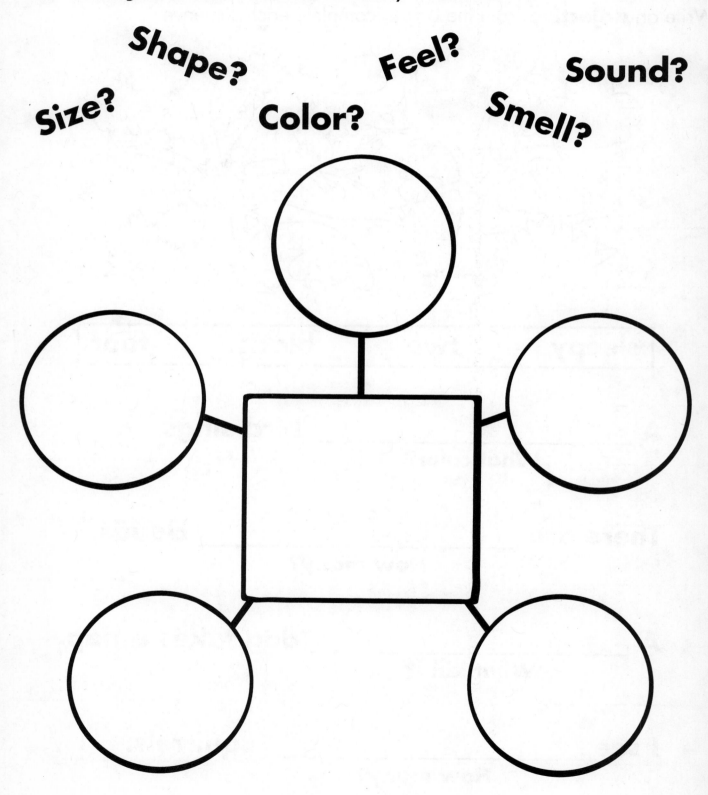

Size? Shape? Color? Feel? Smell? Sound?

Using a graphic organizer to plan a description

# Write About Your Toy

On page 36 you wrote **adjectives** that tell about your toy.
Use them to write sentences about your toy on the lines below.
Then draw a picture of your toy in the box.

The name
of my toy is

# Goldilocks and the Three Bears, Part 1

Fill in the missing words in the story and then read it aloud.

**Mother Bear**   **Goldilocks**

 **Father Bear**  **Baby Bear**

The  _____ **(had, hid)** a little

_____ **(in, on)** the woods.

One day _____ **(Mother, mixer)** Bear

said, "I will _____ **(fax, fix)** a ⌣ for you."

But the ⌣ was too _____ **(hit, hot)**. So the

_____ **(went, want)** for a walk.

A little _____ **(green, girl)** named Goldilocks

was _____ **(last, lost)** in the woods. Goldilocks

saw the ⌂ and went _____ **(in, on)**.

Reading a story and supplying missing words

# Goldilocks and the Three Bears, Part 2

Goldilocks _____ (sat, sot) in Baby Bear's

. She was too _____ (bag, big)

for the and _____ (at, it) broke.

Goldilocks saw the that was _____

(sat, set) out to cool. She ate _____ (all, ill) of

Baby Bear's ! Then she laid _____

(down, duck) on Baby Bear's _____ (bad, bed).

The came _____ (back, buck).

They saw the and the . Baby Bear was

_____ (sad, sod). His _____ (dad, did)

was _____ (mud, mad).

Then the saw Goldilocks

_____ (and, end) she saw them. Goldilocks

jumped _____ (up, us) and ran away—

_____ (fast, fist)!

The _____ (End, And)!

# What Happened in the Woods?

Read the story.

**Dan took a walk in the woods. First he saw a bird. Then he saw a deer. Next he saw a bunny. Finally Dan saw a skunk, and he ran away!**

The pictures show the **events** in the story. The **events** are the things that happen in the story. Number the **events** in order from **1** to **4**. Then color the pictures.

Understanding story sequence

# What's the Main Idea?

The **main idea** is the most important idea.

Read each sentence. Circle the **main idea** of each picture.

**The giant is happy.**

**The giant eats a lot.**

**The clown is sad.**

**The clown is funny.**

**We have lots of fruit.**

**We ate all our fruit.**

**My friend moved away.**

**My friend will be home soon.**

# Choosing the Main Idea

Read each story. Circle the sentence that tells the **main idea**.

It is raining. Ann puts on boots. She puts on a raincoat. She puts on a hat. Now she is ready.

**Ann dresses for a rainy day.**

**Ann takes a long time to dress.**

The house is old. It needs new paint. The windows are broken. The door is loose. The roof has holes.

**The house is old but nice.**

**The old house needs to be fixed.**

Identifying the main idea of a paragraph

# Give Me the Details!

A **detail** is a fact that tells more about the **main idea**.

Look for **details** as you read this short story.

This is my cat, Tiger. He has soft fur. He has stripes. He has a long tail. He sleeps on my bed at night. He purrs in my ear to wake me up. He is a good friend.

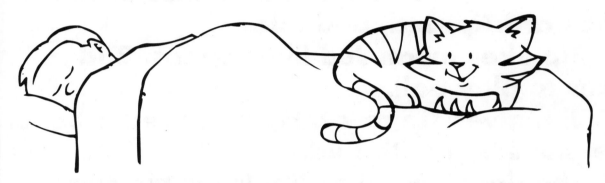

Circle the answers.

| | |
|---|---|
| **What is the name of the cat?** | **Tiger** <br> **Kitty** |
| **What is his fur like?** | **rough** <br> **soft** |
| **What is his tail like?** | **long** <br> **short** |
| **Where does he sleep?** | **on the bed** <br> **in a box** |

# Story Memory

Read the story.

Jim has three dogs. The names of the dogs are Tip, Jed, and Bud.

Tip likes meat. Jed likes bones. Bud likes to play ball.

Jim gives Tip meat. He gives Jed a bone. He plays ball with Bud.

The dogs love Jim. Jim loves his dogs.

Write a complete sentence to answer each question correctly.

**What does Bud like to do?**

_____

**What does Jim give Jed?**

_____

**What does Jim like to play with Bud?**

_____

# Then What Happened?

Read this part of a story. Think about what might happen next.

**The puppy has been told many times not to sit on the new chair. But one day he is home alone. He wants to take a nap. The chair looks so soft.**

Draw a picture of what you think will happen next.

Write about what you think will happen next.

_____

_____

_____

_____

# Picture Detective

Use the picture clues to guess what is happening. Circle the guess that fits the clues.

**This girl likes carrots.**

**This girl does not like carrots.**

**Today is windy.**

**There is no wind today.**

**The bag is heavy.**

**The bag is light.**

**The team just lost the game.**

**The team just won the game.**

**The girl will go out to play.**

**The girl will stay home from school.**

*Making inferences using visual clues*

# What Caused This?

A **cause** is the reason why something happens.
An **effect** is what happens.

**Cause:** ⟶ **Effect:**
Jenny gave her flower water.

The flower grew tall and strong.

Draw a line to match each **cause** with its **effect**.

## CAUSE                    ## EFFECT

 **Bear was hungry.**

**He got a sunburn.**

 **Bear was tired.**

**He ate a big meal.**

 **Bear sat in the sun.**

**He got lost.**

 **Bear went far away.**

**He went to bed.**

Understanding cause and effect

# Discover Why

Look at the picture. Use the clues to discover **causes** and **effects**.

Draw a line between each **effect** and its **cause**.

## EFFECT

**The boy runs.**

**The girl is mad.**

**The baby yawns.**

**The man smiles.**

## CAUSE

**She is sleepy.**

**He is getting a present.**

**She fell into the pond.**

**He is being chased by bees.**

Understanding cause and effect

# S and Two Partners

Some **blends** join **s** with *two* other consonants.

He has **str**ing, a **spr**ing, and a **scr**ew.

Read the words in the box. Write a word from the box to name each picture. Then circle the three-consonant **blend** at the beginning of each word you wrote.

| spray | scrub | strong | straw |

---

Reviewing three-consonant blends with **s**

# You're Doing Great!

To make a **contraction**, you put two words together. You leave out one or more letters and put in this mark ' instead. This mark ' is called an **apostrophe**.

| | |
|---|---|
| we've = we have | let's = let us |
| she's = she is | you're = you are |
| we're = we are | I'll = I will |
| don't = do not | won't = will not |

Read the sentences. Circle two words that can be made into a **contraction**. Write the **contraction** on the line.

We are having pizza for dinner. _____

Let us help mom fix it. _____

I will get the sauce and cheese. _____

We have no pepperoni! _____

Dad will not go to the store. _____

You are putting it in the oven. _____

This is hot! Do not burn yourself! _____

She is the best cook! _____

# Yum! It's Lunch Time

Read each sentence. Put a **period**, **question mark**, or **exclamation point** at the end to complete it.

The pie is really hot____

What kind of pie is it____

I bought a hot dog____

May I sit here____

I'm so hungry____

Hurry and eat____

Lisa likes milk____

Her cupcake is chocolate____

Do you see Sam____

Isn't he silly____

Sam likes fruit____

He hasn't eaten____

# Capital Review

Rewrite each sentence correctly.

**bob put on a mask.**

_____

**I bought this book on tuesday.**

_____

**the baby horse is cute.**

_____

**I want to visit alaska.**

_____

**I go to the store with mom.**

_____

**april is a rainy month.**

_____

Reviewing capitalization

# Searching for Plural Nouns

Read the **nouns** in the box. Find and circle the **plural** form of each noun in the puzzle. The words may go across or down.

| baby | ball | box | bus | city |
|------|------|-----|-----|------|
| fly | mouse | man | pail | snake |

```
m  o  u  s  e  s  e  s  m  a  n
s  n  a  b  a  l  l  s  c
b  o  x  e  s  n  o  p  i
a  m  i  c  e  a  s  a  t
b  x  s  i  a  k  n  i  y
i  b  o  t  m  e  a  l  s
e  f  l  i  e  s  k  s  k
s  b  a  e  n  d  e  n  e
y  b  u  s  e  s  s  o  x
```

# Animals Play

**Remember:**
A **verb** ending in **s** usually tells about one person or thing.
A **verb** not ending in **s** usually tells about more than one.

**One bird sings.**          **Three birds sing.**

Read the first sentence in each row and underline the verb. Rewrite the verb to fit the second sentence.

**One ant crawls. Several ants** _____.

**Three ducks swim. One duck** _____.

**One bunny hops. Many bunnies** _____.

**Lots of flowers grow. One flower** _____.

Review correct subject and verb agreement

# Shopping for Verbs

Read the sentences. Circle the **verb** that correctly completes each sentence.

Many people **come / comes** to the store.

He **place / places** boxes on the shelf.

Dad **chooses / choose** a box.

The cart **has / have** wheels.

The clerk **do / does** her job.

Dad **carries / carry** the bag.

# Let's Go to the Zoo!

Write a **noun** or **verb** from the box to complete each sentence.

| ape | bear | made | went | were |
|-----|------|------|------|------|

We _____ to the zoo.
verb

I waved to the _____.
noun

The monkeys _____ me laugh.
verb

The _____ was asleep.
noun

The hippos _____ fat.
verb

Reviewing sentences with nouns and verbs

# A Fish Story

Read the short story.
Circle all the **nouns**.
Underline all the **verbs**.

Hal likes to fish in the brook.

The water is clean. The water is cold.

There are lots of fish in the water.

Hal feels a fish tug the line. Hal

catches the fish. Then he puts it back

into the clean, cold water. It is too

small to keep.

2. Review

# The Deep, Blue Sea

Read the sentences. Circle two **adjectives** in each sentence.

**Two**  **swim under deep water.**

**Long** 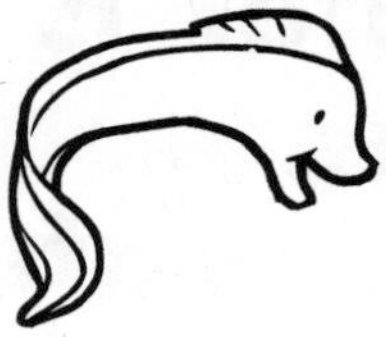 **s play by the old ship.**

**Are those round**  **s in the open chest?**

**One clam sits on the smooth sand.**

**Tall**  **s grow in the cool sea.**

**Three happy**  **s play.**



Reviewing adjectives in sentences

# A Surprise Box

Read each sentence and draw a line to its matching picture. Then number the **events** in order from **1** to **4**.

**Kate finds a wrapped box.**

**Kate puts the hat on and laughs.**

**Kate opens the box carefully.**

**Kate sees a fun hat in the box.**

# You've Got the Right Idea

The **main idea** of a story is its most important idea.

Each row of pictures tells a story. Underline the sentence that tells the **main idea** of each story.

**The party was fun.**

**Jake wore a party hat.**

**No one had fun at the party.**

**The cake was big.**

**The kittens were white.**

**Sue gave away three kittens.**

**The kittens were small.**

**Sue kept three kittens.**

# Answer Key

Please take time to review the work your child has completed and remember to praise both success and effort. If your child makes a mistake, let him or her know that mistakes are a part of learning. Then explain the correct answer and how to find it. Taking the time to help your child and an active interest in his or her progress shows that you feel learning is important.

**page 1**

### The Blend Tree

Look at the words on the apples. If you see a **blend** at the beginning of the word, color the apple red. If you see a **blend** at the end of the word, color the apple yellow. Then color the rest of the picture.

Recognizing consonant blends: initial and final position   1

**page 2**

### A Barn on a Farm

Usually, **ar** has the vowel sound you hear in **barn**.

barn

Circle the correct name for each picture.

| aim | **arm** | pack | **park** | **star** | stay |
| make | **mark** | cat | cart | **party** | pantry |

Write **ar** to complete each word below. Then read the words aloud.

March   start   large

shark   dark   part

Recognizing the sounds of r-controlled vowels   2

**page 3**

### Blow Your Horn for or!

Usually, **or** has the vowel sound you hear in **horn**.

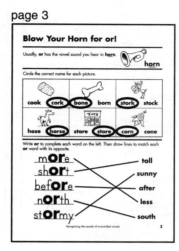

horn

Circle the correct name for each picture.

cook (cork) (bone) born (stork) stock

hose (horse) stare (store) (corn) cone

Write **or** to complete each word on the left. Then draw lines to match each **or** word with its opposite.

m**or**e ——— tall
sh**or**t ——— sunny
bef**or**e ——— after
n**or**th ——— less
st**or**my ——— south

Recognizing the sounds of r-controlled vowels   3

**page 4**

### The Early Bird Gets the Worm

The vowel sound is the same in each of the words below.

bird   worm   turn   fern   earth

The **ar** in **backward** also has this vowel sound.   backward

Answer each riddle using one of the words from above.

I am part of the solar system. **earth**
I live in the dirt. **worm**
I like to chirp. **bird**
I am the opposite of forward. **backward**

Circle the words that have the same vowel sound that you hear in **earth**.

(nurse) (fur) four (forward)
(burn) more (girl) (word)

4   Recognizing the sounds of r-controlled vowels

**page 5**

### Different Letters, Same Sound

Usually, **aw** and **au** have the same vowel sound you hear in the words **saw** and **automobile**.

saw

automobile

Often, **al** has the same sound.

call   talk

Read the words in the box. Circle the letters that stand for the same vowel sound in each word. Write a word from the box to name each picture.

(al) (all) (al) (aw) (au) (aw)

ball   walk

yawn   hawk

Recognizing the vowel digraphs al, au, and aw   5

**page 6**

### How About ow and ou?

Both **ow** and **ou** can have the same vowel sound.

brown   round

Read each word. Underline **ow** or **ou** in each word.

h**ow**   ab**ou**t   l**ou**d   fl**ow**er
c**ow**boy   h**ou**se   d**ow**n   m**ou**th   f**ou**nd

Read each sentence. Circle the words that are misspelled and rewrite them correctly on the lines.

The (cloun) likes to laugh and (showt).
clown   shout

The (cowboy) sniffs the (flour.)
cowboy   flower

(Nou) we will sit on the (grownd.)
Now   ground

6   Recognizing the diphthongs ow and ou

**page 7**

### Ought We to Trust ou?

There are different sounds for **ou**. Say each word below and listen for the **ou** sound.

could   couch   cough

When **ou** is followed by **ght**, the **gh** is silent and only the **t** is heard.

She b**ou**ght skates.

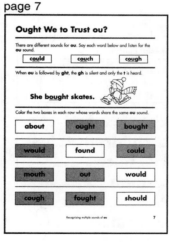

Color the two boxes in each row whose words share the same **ou** sound.

| about | ought | bought |
| would | found | could |
| mouth | out | would |
| cough | fought | should |

Recognizing multiple sounds of ou   7

**page 8**

### Looking at oo

In some words, **oo** has the vowel sound you hear in the word **look**.

look   hood
brook

Match each word with its picture.

book
cookie
foot
hood
hook
wood

Underline each word with the same vowel sound as **foot**.

stood   took   tooth   good   boot   look

8   Recognizing the short double o sound of oo

**page 9**

### Some Special Words

The words in the box below all have the same vowel sound as **look**. Read each word and underline the letter or letters that stand for the vowel sound you hear in **look**.

| could | would | bull |
| put | should | full |

The **l** in the words **could**, **would**, and **should** is silent—it has no sound.

Circle the word that best completes each sentence. Write the word on the line.

The box is **full** of pens.
(full) pull

The big **bull** has horns.
(bull) could

You **should** be kind to pets.
(should) would

I **put** my bike away.
pull (put)

Recognizing the short double oo sound of ou and oo   9

**page 10**

### The Joyful Noise of oi and oy!

Both **oi** and **oy** have the same vowel sound.

boy   boil

Read each word. Underline **oi** or **oy** in each word.

**oi**l   ch**oi**ce   n**oi**se   p**oi**nt
j**oi**n   ann**oy**   t**oy**   j**oy**

Read each sentence. Circle the words that have the same sound you hear in the word **boy**. Write the words on the lines.

(Roy) ate a (boil) hot dog.
Roy   boil

An (oyster) will not (spoil.)
oyster   spoil

The (cowboy) lost his ten (coins.)
cowboy   coins

10   Recognizing the diphthongs oi and oy

**page 11**

### A Moose on the Moon

In some words, **oo** has the vowel sound you hear in **moon**.

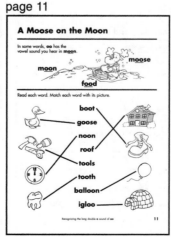

moon   moose
food

Read each word. Match each word with its picture.

boot
goose
noon
roof
tools
tooth
balloon
igloo

Recognizing the long double o sound of oo   11

**page 12**

### Let's Buy Some New Glue

Often, **ew** and **ue** have the same vowel sound as the **oo** in **moon**.

New Glue on *Sale!*

new   glue

Choose a word that best completes each sentence and write it on the line.

We colored the sky **blue**
blew   bloom   (blue)

Ron **drew** a picture.
(drew) droop   due

Mom put meat in the **stew**
clue   gloom   (stew)

Anna **threw** the ball.
true   (threw)   troop

12   Recognizing the long double o sound of ew and ue

Answers   **61**

## page 13

### You're Making Contractions

A **contraction** is two words put together. One or more letters are left out. In their place is this mark ' called **an apostrophe**.

apostrophe
she will = she + wi͟l͟l͟ = **she'll**

**She'll** eat vegetables anytime!

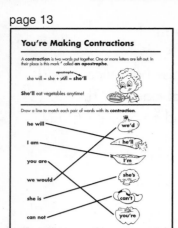

Draw a line to match each pair of words with its **contraction**.

he will — we'd
I am — he'll
you are — I'm
we would — she's
she is — can't
can not — you're

Understanding contractions  13

## page 14

### Nice Ice

Every **statement** ends with a **period**. I like the shiny ice.

Every **question** ends with a **question mark**. Do you think the ice is nice?

Put a **period** or **question mark** at the end of each sentence.

The day is cold **.**
Did the lake freeze **?**
Bob has a new hat **.**
Who will win the race **?**
Can you ice skate **?**
The dog slips **.**

14  Using correct punctuation with statements and questions

## page 15

### Awesome!

A sentence that shows excitement is called an **exclamation**. Every **exclamation** begins with a capital letter and ends with an **exclamation point**.

capital letter

**Watch out!**

exclamation point

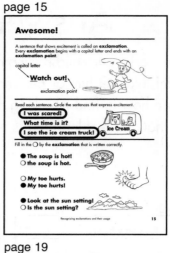

Read each sentence. Circle the sentences that express excitement.

I was scared!
What time is it?
I see the ice cream truck!

Ice Cream

Fill in the ○ by the **exclamation** that is written correctly.

● The soup is hot!
○ the soup is hot.

○ My toe hurts.
● My toe hurts!

● Look at the sun setting!
○ Is the sun setting?

Recognizing exclamations and their usage  15

## page 16

### Start with a Capital

The first word in a sentence always begins with a **capital** letter.

**This** pig is fat.   **The** store is open.

Rewrite each sentence correctly.

cake is yummy.
**Cake is yummy.**

use a pen to write.
**Use a pen to write.**

bill digs a hole.
**Bill digs a hole.**

the pin is sharp!
**The pin is sharp!**

my fish's name is Goldy.
**My fish's name is Goldy.**

this peach is very juicy.
**This peach is very juicy.**

16  Using a capital letter at the beginning of a sentence

## page 17

### Proper Nouns Use Capitals

A **proper noun** is the name of a specific person, place, or thing. Your name is a **proper noun**.

Every **proper noun** begins with a capital letter.

**United States**     **June**

Underline the **proper noun** in each sentence that is not written correctly.

The train goes to boston.
maria ran home.
I was born on june 2, 1997.
This man lives in japan.
My cat's name is misty.
ken has a red bike.

Recognizing proper nouns and their use of capitalization  17

## page 18

### How Many?

A **noun** that names "more than one" is a **plural noun**. To make many **nouns** mean "more than one," add **s** at the end.

**one bear**     **three bears**

Look at the picture. Then read the questions and circle the answers.

1. Look for a cap. How many do you see?
   one cap   two caps   (three caps)

2. Look for a rope. How many do you see?
   (one rope)   two ropes   three ropes

3. Look for a mat. How many do you see?
   one mat   (two mats)   three mats

4. Look for a ball. How many do you see?
   one ball   (two balls)   three balls

18  Forming plurals of regular nouns by adding s

## page 19

### Not Just One

Add **es** to a **noun** ending in **s**, **x**, **ch**, or **sh** to make it a **plural noun**.

one dress   two dresses   one fox   two foxes

Rewrite each **noun**, adding **es** to the end to make it **plural**.

match **matches**
bus **buses**
brush **brushes**
box **boxes**
glass **glasses**

Adding -es to form plurals of nouns ending in s, x, ch, sh  19

## page 20

### Changes for y

Sometimes **y** comes after a consonant at the end of a **noun**. To make these nouns plural, change the **y** to **i** and add **es**.

one bunny   bunn**y͟** + es = bunnies   two bunnies

Rewrite each **noun** to make it **plural**.

candy  **candies**       fly  **flies**
baby  **babies**         berry  **berries**
kitty  **kitties**        lady  **ladies**

20  Forming plurals of nouns ending in y after a consonant

## page 21

### Making Plurals

Read the nouns inside the ◇s. Circle the correct **plural** form of each one.

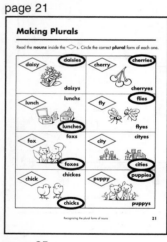

| | |
|---|---|
| daisy — (daisies) / daisys | cherry — (cherries) / cherryes |
| lunch — lunchs / (lunches) | fly — (flies) / flyes |
| fox — foxs / (foxes) | city — cityes / (cities) |
| chick — chickes / (chicks) | puppy — (puppies) / puppys |

Recognizing the plural forms of nouns  21

## page 22

### Special Plurals

Some **nouns** have a special **plural** form.

| One | More Than One |
|---|---|
| man | men |
| woman | women |
| child | children |
| mouse | mice |
| foot | feet |
| tooth | teeth |

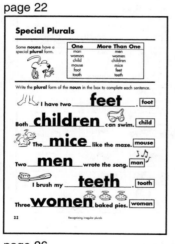

Write the **plural** form of the **noun** in the box to complete each sentence.

I have two **feet** [foot]
Both **children** can swim. [child]
The **mice** like the maze. [mouse]
Two **men** wrote the song. [man]
I brush my **teeth** [tooth]
Three **women** baked pies. [woman]

22  Recognizing irregular plurals

## page 23

### More Special Plurals

A few **nouns** do not change in their **plural** form.

| One | More Than One |
|---|---|
| deer | deer |
| fish | fish |
| moose | moose |
| scissors | scissors |
| sheep | sheep |

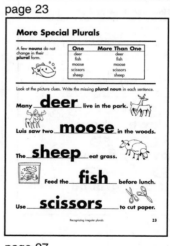

Look at the picture clues. Write the missing **plural noun** in each sentence.

Many **deer** live in the park.
Luis saw two **moose** in the woods.
The **sheep** eat grass.
Feed the **fish** before lunch.
Use **scissors** to cut paper.

Recognizing irregular plurals  23

## page 24

### Bears in Space

A **verb** usually ends in **s** when it tells about only one. It usually does not end in **s** when it tells about more than one.

One star **twinkles**.     Stars **twinkle**.

Circle the correct **verb** to complete each sentence. Then color the picture.

Young Bear _____ a helmet.
wear  (wears)

Mom and Dad Bear _____ photos.
(take)  takes

They all _____ in space.
floats  (float)

Young Bear _____ space.
(likes)  like

Mom and Dad Bear _____ space, too.
likes  (like)

24  Choosing the correct verb form to agree with the subject

## page 25

### Which Sounds Correct?

Read each sentence. Fill in the ○ by the sentence that uses the correct **verb**.

● The children like art.
○ The children likes art.

○ Maria paint a flower.
● Maria paints a flower.

○ A boy use clay.
● A boy uses clay.

● Two boys draw cars.
○ Two boys draws cars.

● The teacher hangs up the art.
○ The teacher hang up the art.

○ They all works hard.
● They all work hard.

Choosing the correct verb form to agree with the subject  25

## page 26

### Am, Are, and Is

**Verbs** may also tell what a person or thing is. We use the verbs **am**, **are**, and **is** to do this.

| Verb Chart | |
|---|---|
| I | am |
| You | are |
| He, She, or It | is |
| We | are |
| They | are |

Use **am** with **I** when you tell about yourself.
I **am** happy!

Use **is** with **he**, **she**, or **it** when you tell about another person or thing.
He **is** happy!

Use **are** with **you** or when you tell about more than one.
The dogs **are** happy!

Write **am**, **are**, or **is** to complete each sentence.

Leaves **are** green.     I **am** smart.
Nan **is** a girl.         Candy **is** sweet.
We **are** friends.       You **are** nice.

26  Using am, are, and is: present tense forms of the verb to be

## page 27

### You Are Smart!

Read each sentence. Fill in the ○ by the sentence that uses the correct **verb**.

● I am your friend.
○ I is your friend.

○ You is the winner!
● You are the winner!

● Brian is a good kicker.
○ Brian are a good kicker.

● The puppy is tiny.
○ The puppy are tiny.

● We are sleepy.
○ We is sleepy.

Using am, are, and is: present tense forms of the verb to be  27

## page 28

### Has or Have?

**Verbs** may also tell what a person or thing has. We use the verbs **has** and **have** to do this.

Use **has** with **he**, **she**, or **it**.
Use **has** with a noun that names one.
He **has** a tail.
The squirrel **has** a tail.

Use **have** with **I**, **you**, **we**, or **they**.
Use **have** with a plural noun.
They **have** tails.
The squirrels **have** tails.

| has | have |
|---|---|
| he, she, it | I, you, we, they |
| noun | plural noun |

Read each sentence. Fill in the ○ by the sentence that uses the correct **verb**.

● A dog has a tail.
○ A dog have a tail.

● He has a new bike.
○ He have a new bike.

● They have gone home.
○ They has gone home.

○ Birds has wings.
● Birds have wings.

28  Using has and have: present tense forms of the verb to have

**62**                    Answers

## page 29

### Have Fun!

Write **has** or **have** to complete each sentence.

The panda **has** a baby.

Nuts **have** hard shells.

He **has** broken the law.

The shaker **has** salt in it.

They **have** launched the rocket.

The crabs **have** claws.

Using **has** and **have**: present tense forms of the verb **to have**    29

## page 30

### Does and Do

Use **does** with **he**, **she**, or **it**.    He **does** his job.
Use **does** with a noun that names one.    The man **does** his job.

Use **do** with **I**, **you**,    They **do** good work.
**we**, or **they**.    The people **do** good work.
Use **do** with a plural noun.

| does | do |
|---|---|
| he, she, it | I, you, we, they |
| noun | plural noun |

Write **does** or **do** to complete each sentence.

Children **do** like to play games.

She **does** tricks.

I **do** my homework.

Tim **does** his chores.

30    Using **does** and **do**: present tense forms of the verb **to do**

## page 31

### Do Your Best!

Write **does** or **do** to complete each sentence.

This hat **does** not have stripes.

Fairies **do** magic.

Mom **does** like to read.

Clowns **do** funny tricks.

Ann **does** skate well.

Tom **does** like to eat cake.

Using **does** and **do**: present tense forms of the verb **to do**    31

## page 32

### Let's Go to the Movies!

Write a **noun** or **verb** from the box to complete each sentence.

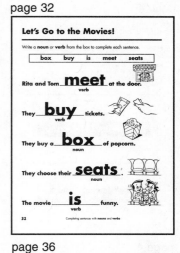

| box | buy | is | meet | seats |
|---|---|---|---|---|

Rita and Tom **meet** at the door.
    *verb*

They **buy** tickets.
   *verb*

They buy a **box** of popcorn.
      *noun*

They choose their **seats**.
        *noun*

The movie **is** funny.
     *verb*

32    Completing sentences with **nouns** and **verbs**

## page 33

### Pete and Pat

Read the short story.
Circle the correct **noun** or **verb**
to complete each sentence.
Then color the picture.

Pete (**has**, have) a dog. The dog (**is**, am) tan and black. Her name is Pat.

Pat (like, **likes**) to run. Her (**tail**, tails) wags when she (**run**, runs) Pat likes to chew (bone, **bones**) Pete (give, **gives**) her a bone every (**day**, dry). Pat likes to (play, **play**). Pete throws a (**ball**, bull) to her. Pat likes that (**game**, gum).

Pat (love, **loves**) Pete. Pete (**loves**, love) Pat. They are best (**friends**, friend).

Completing a short story with nouns and verbs    33

## page 34

### Words that Describe

Some words tell more about nouns.
They are called **adjectives**.
**Adjectives** can answer these questions:

What kind?    How many?    What color?
**fuzzy** bears    **two** bears    **white** bears

Read each sentence. Circle the **adjective** in each sentence.

This is a **pretty** flower.
It has **two** leaves.

I see **tiny** mice.
I see **three** mice.

She has **long** hair.
She has **big** eyes.

The bus is **big**.
The wheels are **black**.

34    Recognizing adjectives

## page 35

### A Sunny Afternoon

**Adjectives** tell more about nouns.

Write an **adjective** from the box to complete each sentence.

| sleepy | two | black | four |
|---|---|---|---|

A **black** bird sings.
   *What color?*

There are **four** clouds.
        *How many?*

A **sleepy** dog takes a nap.
   *What kind?*

I see **two** squirrels.
     *How many?*

Choosing adjectives to complete sentences    35

## page 36

### Tell About a Toy

Write the name of a toy you like in the square.
Write an **adjective** that tells about the toy in each circle.

Shape?   Feel?   Sound?
Size?   Color?   Smell?

**Answers will vary.**

36    Using a graphic organizer to plan a description

## page 37

### Write About Your Toy

On page 36 you wrote **adjectives** that tell about your toy.
Use them to write sentences about your toy on the lines below.
Then draw a picture of your toy in the box.

The name
of my toy is

**Answers will vary.**

Using a graphic organizer to write a description    37

## page 38

### Goldilocks and the Three Bears, Part 1

Fill in the missing words in the story and then read it aloud.

Mother Bear     Goldilocks

Father Bear     Baby Bear

The 🐻🐻🐻 **had** (had, hid) a little **in** (in, on) the woods.
One day **Mother** (Mother, mixer) Bear said, "I will **fix** (fax, fix) a 🍲 for you."
But the 🍲 was too **hot** (hit, hot). So the 🐻🐻🐻 **went** (went, want) for a walk.
A little **girl** (green, girl) named Goldilocks was **lost** (last, lost) in the woods. Goldilocks saw the 🏠 and went **in** (in, on).

38    Reading a story and supplying missing words

## page 39

### Goldilocks and the Three Bears, Part 2

Goldilocks **sat** (sat, sot) in Baby Bear's 🪑. She was too **big** (bag, big) for the 🪑 and **it** (at, it) broke.
Goldilocks saw the 🍲 that was **set** (sat, set) out to cool. She ate **all** (all, ill) of Baby Bear's 🍲! Then she laid **down** (down, duck) on Baby Bear's 🛏️ **bed** (bad, bed).
They saw the 🪑 and the 🍲. Baby Bear was **sad** (sad, sod). His **dad** (dad, did) was **mad** (mud, mad).
Then the 🐻🐻🐻 saw Goldilocks **and** (and, end) she saw them. Goldilocks jumped **up** (up, us) and ran away— **fast** (fast, fist)!
The **End** (End, And)!

Reading a story and supplying missing words    39

## page 40

### What Happened in the Woods?

Read the story.

Dan took a walk in the woods. First he saw a bird. Then he saw a deer. Next he saw a bunny. Finally Dan saw a skunk, and he ran away!

The pictures show the **events** in the story. The **events** are the things that happen in the story. Number the **events** in order from **1** to **4**. Then color the pictures.

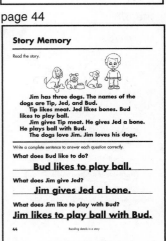

40    Understanding story sequence

## page 41

### What's the Main Idea?

The **main idea** is the most important idea.

Read each sentence. Circle the **main idea** of each picture.

**The giant is happy.**
The giant eats a lot.

The clown is sad.
**The clown is funny.**

We have lots of fruit.
**We ate all our fruit.**

**My friend moved away.**
My friend will be home soon.

Identifying main ideas    41

## page 42

### Choosing the Main Idea

Read each story. Circle the sentence that tells the **main idea**.

It is raining. Ann puts on boots. She puts on a raincoat. She puts on a hat. Now she is ready.

**Ann dresses for a rainy day.**
Ann takes a long time to dress.

The house is old. It needs new paint. The windows are broken. The door is loose. The roof has holes.

The house is old but nice.
**The old house needs to be fixed.**

42    Identifying the main idea of a paragraph

## page 43

### Give Me the Details!

A **detail** is a fact that tells more about the **main idea**.

Look for **details** as you read this short story.

This is my cat, Tiger. He has soft fur. He has stripes. He has a long tail. He sleeps on my bed at night. He purrs in my ear to wake me up. He is a good friend.

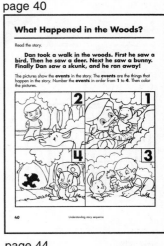

Circle the answers.

What is the name of the cat?    **Tiger**   Kitty

What is his fur like?    rough   **soft**

What is his tail like?    **long**   short

Where does he sleep?    **on the bed**   in a box

Recognizing details in a story    43

## page 44

### Story Memory

Read the story.

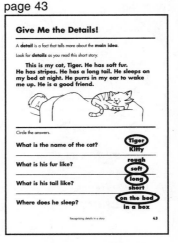

Jim has three dogs. The names of the dogs are Tip, Jed, and Bud.
Tip likes meat. Jed likes bones. Bud likes to play ball.
Jim gives Tip meat. He gives Jed a bone. He plays ball with Bud.
The dogs love Jim. Jim loves his dogs.

Write a complete sentence to answer each question correctly.

What does Bud like to do?
**Bud likes to play ball.**

What does Jim give Jed?
**Jim gives Jed a bone.**

What does Jim like to play with Bud?
**Jim likes to play ball with Bud.**

44    Recalling details in a story

Answers

**63**

### Then What Happened?

Read this part of a story. Think about what might happen next.

The puppy has been told many times not to sit on the new chair. But one day he is home alone. He wants to take a nap. The chair looks so soft.

Draw a picture of what you think will happen next.

**Answers will vary.**

Write about what you think will happen next.

**Answers will vary.**

Predicting outcomes 45

### Picture Detective

Use the picture clues to guess what is happening. Circle the guess that fits the clues.

This girl likes carrots.
(This girl does not like carrots.)

(Today is windy.)
There is no wind today.

The bag is heavy.
(The bag is light.)

The team just lost the game.
(The team just won the game.)

The girl will go out to play.
(The girl will stay home from school.)

46 Making inferences using visual clues

### What Caused This?

A **cause** is the reason why something happens. An **effect** is what happens.

Cause: Jenny gave her flower water.
Effect: The flower grew tall and strong.

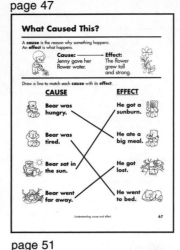

Draw a line to match each **cause** with its **effect**.

| CAUSE | EFFECT |
|---|---|
| Bear was hungry. | He got a sunburn. |
| Bear was tired. | He ate a big meal. |
| Bear sat in the sun. | He got lost. |
| Bear went far away. | He went to bed. |

Understanding cause and effect 47

### Discover Why

Look at the picture. Use the clues to discover **causes** and **effects**.

Draw a line between each **effect** and its **cause**.

| EFFECT | CAUSE |
|---|---|
| The boy runs. | She is sleepy. |
| The girl is mad. | He is getting a present. |
| The baby yawns. | She fell into the pond. |
| The man smiles. | He is being chased by bees. |

48 Understanding cause and effect

### S and Two Partners

Some **blends** join **s** with two other consonants.

He has **string**, a **spring**, and a **screw**.

Read the words in the box. Write a word from the box to name each picture. Then circle the three-consonant **blend** at the beginning of each word you wrote.

| spray | scrub | strong | straw |
|---|---|---|---|

**straw**     **spray**

**scrub**     **strong**

Reviewing three-consonant blends with s 49

### You're Doing Great!

To make a **contraction**, you put two words together. You leave out one or more letters and put in this mark ' instead. This mark ' is called an **apostrophe**.

| we've = we have | let's = let us |
|---|---|
| she's = she is | you're = you are |
| we're = we are | I'll = I will |
| don't = do not | won't = will not |

Read the sentences. Circle two words that can be made into a **contraction**. Write the **contraction** on the line.

(We are) having pizza for dinner. **We're**

(Let us) help mom fix it. **Let's**

(I will) get the sauce and cheese. **I'll**

(We have) no pepperoni. **We've**

Dad (will not) go to the store. **won't**

(You are) putting it in the oven. **You're**

This is hot. (Do not) burn yourself! **Don't**

(She is) the best cook! **She's**

50 Reviewing contractions

### Yum! It's Lunch Time

Read each sentence. Put a **period**, **question mark**, or **exclamation point** at the end to complete it.

The pie is really hot **!**

What kind of pie is it **?**

I bought a hot dog **.**

May I sit here **?**

I'm so hungry **!**

Hurry and eat **!**

Lisa likes milk **.**

Her cupcake is chocolate **.**

Do you see Sam **?**

Isn't he silly **?**

Sam likes fruit **.**

He hasn't eaten **.**

Reviewing types of sentences: statements, questions, and exclamations 51

### Capital Review

Rewrite each sentence correctly.

bob put on a mask.
**Bob put on a mask.**

I bought this book on tuesday.
**I bought this book on Tuesday.**

the baby horse is cute.
**The baby horse is cute.**

I want to visit alaska.
**I want to visit Alaska.**

I go to the store with mom.
**I go to the store with Mom.**

april is a rainy month.
**April is a rainy month.**

52 Reviewing capitalization

### Searching for Plural Nouns

Read the **nouns** in the box. Find and circle the **plural** form of each noun in the puzzle. The words may go across or down.

| baby | ball | box | bus | city |
|---|---|---|---|---|
| fly | mouse | man | pail | snake |

| m | o | u | s | e | s | m | a | n |
|---|---|---|---|---|---|---|---|---|
| s | n | a | b | a | l | l | s | c |
| b | o | x | e | s | n | o | p | i |
| a | m | i | c | e | a | s | a | t |
| b | x | s | i | a | k | n | i | y |
| i | b | o | t | m | e | a | l | s |
| e | f | l | i | e | s | k | s | e |
| s | b | a | e | n | d | e | n | o |
| y | b | u | s | e | s | o | x |   |

Reviewing plural nouns 53

### Animals Play

**Remember:**
A **verb** ending in **s** usually tells about one person or thing.
A **verb** not ending in **s** usually tells about more than one.

One bird sings.     Three birds sing.

Read the first sentence in each row and underline the verb. Rewrite the verb to fit the second sentence.

One ant crawls. Several ants **crawl**

Three ducks swim. One duck **swims**

One bunny hops. Many bunnies **hop**

Lots of flowers grow. One flower **grows**

54 Review correct subject and verb agreement

### Shopping for Verbs

Read the sentences. Circle the **verb** that correctly completes each sentence.

Many people (come) comes to the store.

He place (places) boxes on the shelf.

Dad (chooses) choose a box.

The cart (has) have wheels.

The clerk (does) do her job.

Dad (carries) carry the bag.

Review present tense verb-subject agreement 55

### Let's Go to the Zoo!

Write a **noun** or **verb** from the box to complete each sentence.

| ape | bear | made | went | were |
|---|---|---|---|---|

We **went** to the zoo.
verb

I waved to the **ape**.
noun

The monkeys **made** me laugh.
verb

The **bear** was asleep.
noun

The hippos **were** fat.
verb

56 Reviewing sentences with nouns and verbs

### A Fish Story

Read the short story. Circle all the **nouns**. Underline all the **verbs**.

(Hal) likes to fish in the (brook). The (water) is clean. The (water) is cold. There are lots of (fish) in the water. (Hal) feels a (fish) tug the (line). (Hal) catches the (fish). Then he puts it back into the clean, cold (water). (It) is too small to keep.

Reviewing nouns and verbs in a short story 57

### The Deep, Blue Sea

Read the sentences. Circle two **adjectives** in each sentence.

(Two) fish swim under (deep) water.

(Long) eels play by the (old) ship.

Are those (round) shells in the (open) chest?

(One) clam sits on the (smooth) sand.

(Tall) plants grow in the (cool) sea.

(Three) (happy) seahorses play.

58 Reviewing adjectives in sentences

### A Surprise Box

Read each sentence and draw a line to its matching picture. Then number the **events** in order from 1 to 4.

**1** Kate finds a wrapped box.

**4** Kate puts the hat on and laughs.

**2** Kate opens the box carefully.

**3** Kate sees a fun hat in the box.

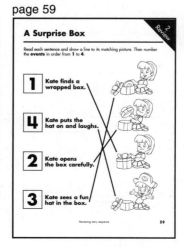

Reviewing story sequence 59

### You've Got the Right Idea

The **main idea** of a story is its most important idea.

Each row of pictures tells a story. Underline the sentence that tells the **main idea** of each story.

The party was fun.     Jake wore a party hat.

No one had fun at the party.     The cake was big.

The kittens were white.     Sue gave away three kittens.

The kittens were small.     Sue kept three kittens.

60 Reviewing the main idea of a story told in pictures